Success
Learn and Practise

English
age 7-8

YEAR 3

Lynn Huggins-Cooper

Contents

Speaking and listening

Word structure and spelling

Sentence structure and punctuation

Understanding text

Creating and shaping texts

Text structure and organisation

Test practice

Glossary

Answers

Speaking and listening

Speaking

Having a conversation is all about taking turns. You need to think carefully about what you say, to make sure that the person you are speaking to will understand you. Then you must listen to their reply, so that you know what to say next.

Taking turns and listening is not just good manners. If you don't do it, you might as well be talking to yourself!

Remember, too, that the kind of information you get back from the person you are speaking to will depend on the questions you ask. Try to ask questions that need a full sentence in reply, rather than just 'yes' or 'no'.

"Are you happy?"   "Yes!"

"Why are you happy?"   "I'm happy because it's my birthday and I'm having a party!"

Listening

Most of us are terrible listeners! Watching TV and playing computer games encourages us to use our eyes, not our ears! It is very easy to focus too much on what you have to say, and not give enough attention to what the person you are speaking to is saying. You can practise listening skills by playing games like Chinese Whispers, where you whisper a message from person to person around the group. Unless everyone listens really carefully, the message that gets to the end of the group won't be right!

You can also throw a ball backwards and forwards as you speak to a partner. When you are holding the ball, it is your turn to speak. When your partner has it, you have to listen.

For a real challenge, play the alphabet game. One player starts by saying 'I went to the shops and I bought . . .' before adding something beginning with the letter A. The next player must repeat what the first player said, before adding something starting with B, and so on. Can you get right through the alphabet without forgetting what other players have bought?

Exercise 1

Speaking

Look at these questions. Circle the ones which will help to keep a conversation going by requiring a longer answer than just 'yes' or 'no'.

a   Do you like playing football?

b   What kinds of films do you like?

c   Why do you think Mrs Brown is so cheerful today?

d   Is it raining?

e   Do you want to play tennis?

f   How do you send an email from this computer?

Exercise 2

Listening

Now see how well you can listen. Ask a helper to gather five everyday objects, without letting you see them. Get your helper to describe what each object looks, feels and smells like. Can you guess what each one is?

Use the table to record useful clue words and what you think each object is.

Object	Useful clue words	I think the object is...
1		
2		
3		
4		
5		

Challenge

Some things are harder to say than others. Tongue-twisters are a great way to practise saying tricky things! Try this one:
Around the ragged rock, the ragged rascal ran!

Brain Teaser

Ask a partner about one of these topics. Listen carefully to their opinion. Do you agree?

What do you think about school uniform?

How much homework should children get?

Prefixes

Prefixes are letters that can be added to the beginning of words. *Pre* means before. It tells us that a prefix comes at the beginning of the word.

Pre is a prefix itself. Think of the words preview, prehistoric and premature. If you don't know what they mean, look them up in a dictionary!

Prefixes give us clues to the meanings of words. If we know what the prefix means, it can help us to understand new words.

For example, *anti* means against. Antidote means medicine used against a poison. Anti-slavery means against, or opposed to, slavery.

prehistoric

antidote

Exercise 1

Underline the prefix for each of these words.

a   unacceptable

b   retake

c   misunderstanding

d   non-flammable

e   anti-inflammatory

f   prepay

g   ex-president

h   prefabricate

i   inaccurate

j   non-smoker

Top Tip

Prefixes can also be used to make new words that have the opposite meaning of the original word:

mis (prefix) + lead = mislead
non (prefix) + sense = nonsense

Exercise 2

Add the prefix *non* or *mis* to these words to make a new word!

a _____ perishable   e _____ stop

b _____ understand   f _____ conductor

c _____ refundable   g _____ fiction

d _____ inform   h _____ behave

Exercise 3

Read the explanation of each word. Then use the correct prefix from the box to complete the words.

| pre | un | anti | in | mis | non |

a _____ historic – before the days recorded by history.

b _____ action – no action.

c _____ understand – not understand.

d _____ sense – making no sense; silly.

e _____ clockwise – moves the other way to clockwise.

f _____ used – not used.

Challenge

Find out about more prefixes, by reading through a newspaper article and underlining all the prefixes you can find.

Brain Teaser

Change these words to mean the opposite of the original meaning by adding a prefix.

1 _____ understanding

2 _____ sense

3 _____ sensitive

4 _____ happy

5 _____ behave

Homonyms and homophones

Homonyms are words that have the same spelling, but mean different things. You can only tell what they mean by looking at the context of the word in the sentence.

Wave can mean:

gesture	motion	shape

Homophones are words that are pronounced alike, but have different meanings or spellings.

to, too and two

which   witch

?

Exercise 1

Match the homonyms to their meanings. Join them with a line.

a Animal skin

b A grand event where people dance

c Something that you chew

d Round toy

e Keep out of sight

f Something that keeps your teeth in place

gum

ball

hide

Exercise 2

Circle the correct word in each sentence. Careful, it's trickier than it looks!

a I'll isle aisle open the door!

b That's really naughty. It's not aloud allowed.

c The alter altar is at the front of the church.

d Spiders have eight ate legs.

e The sun's shining in my I eye aye.

f I kicked the ball bawl.

Top Tip *Have a look at a comic or magazine or newspaper. Underline all of the homonyms on one page. Now see if you can find any homophones.*

Exercise 3

Read the description and circle the word being described.

a A woolly animal that eats grass.   ewe   you   yew

b Something that makes my cat itch!   flee   flea

c The part of Sam's sock that wears out first!   heel   heal

d A noise Mel makes when she has to go to bed.   grown   groan

Challenge

Homonym or homophone? You decide!

1 board and bored

_____

2 buy, by and bye

_____

3 chews and choose

_____

4 currant and current

_____

Brain Teaser

Underline the correct word.

1 If she seas/sees/seize the mouse, she will scream!

2 Which sighed/side of the paper shall I write on?

3 What are their/there/they're names?

4 I want to/two/too go shopping.

Contractions

Contractions are where letters are dropped from words and an **apostrophe** is added to show that letters are missing.

could not	did not	would not	is not
↓	↓	↓	↓
couldn't	didn't	wouldn't	isn't

Exercise 1

Write down the shortened, contracted form of these words.

a must not ➜ _____

b cannot ➜ _____

c is not ➜ _____

d should not ➜ _____

e has not ➜ _____

f you are ➜ _____

g I have ➜ _____

h he has ➜ _____

i have not ➜ _____

Exercise 2

Change these contractions into the longer versions of the words.

a won't _____

b can't _____

c she's _____

d he'll _____

e we've _____

f they'll _____

g hasn't _____

h you're _____

Exercise 3

Write this passage again, changing all of the contractions into the longer versions of the words.

> I don't want to go to the park today. It's boring. My brother hasn't been for ages either. He says there's nowhere to play football.

_____

_____

_____

_____

_____

 Contractions are used in dialogue or informal writing, such as letters to friends. They should not be used in formal writing.

Challenge

Underline the contractions in these sentences and write the full versions of the words below each sentence.

1 I wouldn't like to go.

_____

2 The cat won't go outside.

_____

3 I can't do it!

_____

Brain Teaser

Write the contractions for these words.

1 I have _____

2 we will _____

3 should not _____

4 is not _____

Suffixes

Suffixes are collections of letters that can be added to the end of words.

Suffixes like *ly*, *able*, *ing*, *ful*, *like*, *ic* and *worthy* can often be added to nouns to make **adjectives**.

hope **(noun)** + ful = hopeful **(adjective)**

like **(noun)** + able = likeable **(adjective)**

news **(noun)** + worthy = newsworthy **(adjective)**

Remember, an adjective is a describing word. It describes a **noun**.

Exercise 1

Look at the words below. Next to each one, write down the correct suffix from the box. Then write out the new word that it makes.

> able   ful   ic   ly   worthy

a kind + _____ = _____

b play + _____ = _____

c hero + _____ = _____

d love + _____ = _____

e blame + _____ = _____

> **Top Tip**
>
> Look back to page 4 to remind yourself about prefixes. Remember, a prefix goes at the beginning of an existing word. A suffix goes at the end. An existing word can have a prefix and a suffix, for example <u>un</u>hero<u>ic</u>.

Exercise 2

Write the suffix *ish* or *ful* next to each word to make an adjective.

a baby_____

b child_____

c dread_____

d hope_____

e mourn_____

f wonder_____

g wish_____

h self_____

i boy_____

j tear_____

Exercise 3

Tick the words which make a new word when the suffix *able* is added.

a shock_____ ☐

b like_____ ☐

c break_____ ☐

d hope_____ ☐

e enjoy_____ ☐

f road_____ ☐

g wash_____ ☐

h drink_____ ☐

i jump_____ ☐

Challenge

"I am hopeful that I won't be penniless after pocket money day!"

Underline the suffixes in this sentence.

Brain Teaser

Using the right suffix depends on the sense of the rest of the sentence. Cross out the word from the brackets that is not a real word!

1 The teacher says she gives me jobs to do because I am (trustworthy trustish).

2 That's (wishful wishworthy) thinking!

3 I am completely (penniable penniless) after all that shopping!

Spelling strategy 1

Look/say/cover/write/check **is a great and easy way to learn new spellings!**

Look at the shape of the word.

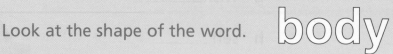

Are there any tails, such as in *y*, or any sticks, such as in *d*? Are there any other shapes, such as *ee* or *oo*, in the middle of the word?

Say the word. **It will help you to remember it. Sound out the syllables to yourself.**

Cover the word. **Can you remember the shape of the word without looking at it? Can you see any tails or sticks? Can you see any other shapes?**

Write the word. **Can you remember it? If there are letters you cannot remember, just write the ones you do remember and leave a space where you think any other letters should go.**

Check the word. **Uncover it. If it is not completely correct, put a tick above the letters you have got right and keep trying!**

Another good way to learn spellings is to look for different words that contain the same sound. Sometimes you just change the first letter and you make a new word!

Exercise 1

Learn these words using look/say/cover/write/check.

a different

b below

c write

d playground

e picture

f remember

g igloo

h christmas

Exercise 2

Now learn these words. Careful, they might be tricky!

a change

b changing

c care

d careful

e carefully

f peace

g peaceful

h peacefully

i event

j eventful

k uneventful

l noisy

m noisily

n noisier

Exercise 3

Look at these words. Write down some new words by changing the first letter. An example has been done for you.

a bat ____fat   cat   hat____

b ball _____

c rut _____

d dad _____

e big _____

f bin _____

g cake _____

Top Tip To learn how to spell long, hard words, split them into sound chunks or syllables. To work out where to split up words, put two fingers underneath your chin and say the word that you want to spell slowly. Get a pen and a piece of paper, and every time your chin drops when you say a sound, it is a part of the word (a syllable). Write the sounds down and it will help you to work out how to spell the word!

Challenge

How many words can you make by changing the first letter of *mad*? Try adding more than one letter to make even more!

Brain Teaser

Write down all of the words you can make by changing the first letter of these words.

1 bid _____

2 bit _____

3 race _____

Spelling strategy 2

Looking for smaller words inside longer words is a great way of improving your spelling!

If you remember the small word and how to spell it, then that's a chunk of a longer, more complicated word you already know how to spell.

How about:

father   ⟶   fat + her

forget   ⟶   for + get

wardrobe   ⟶   ward + robe

tomatoes   ⟶   to, mat, at, toes

pineapples   ⟶   pin, pine, in, apples

Exercise 1

Find two smaller words inside each of these words, then write them down.

a lesson _____ _____

b abundance _____ _____

c history _____ _____

d shell _____ _____

e weather _____ _____

f exchange _____ _____

Exercise 2

Find three smaller words inside each of these longer words, then write them down.

a admittance _____ _____ _____

b electricity _____ _____ _____

c mustard _____ _____ _____

d pricey _____ _____ _____

e splendid _____ _____ _____

f standard _____ _____ _____

Exercise 3

Find four smaller words in each of these words, then write them down.

a another _____ _____ _____ _____

b archive _____ _____ _____ _____

c bulletin _____ _____ _____ _____

d airplane _____ _____ _____ _____

Top Tip *Looking for words within words is great fun! Look in the dictionary for some really long words and see how many words you can find in them.*

Challenge

Does your name or nickname appear in any words? Or are there any words inside your name? Write them here:

Brain Teaser

Write down all of the smaller words you can find in the word **cartridge**.

_____

_____

_____

_____

_____

Verbs

A **verb** is an action (or doing) word. You can make your own writing more interesting if you try to use a variety of verbs instead of using the same ones all of the time.

The girl was shouting (verb) because she saw a spider running (verb) up the wall.

This could be written as:

The girl was shrieking (verb) because she saw a spider scuttling (verb) up the wall.

The second sentence is much more exciting, because the verbs are more descriptive!

Exercise 1

Underline the verbs in these sentences.

a   The boy is racing home.

b   The bat is fluttering in the darkness.

c   The mouse is squeaking.

d   The girl is singing a beautiful song.

e   I walked for miles in the hot sun.

f   The sun is shining brightly.

Remember, a verb is often called a doing word, because it describes the action in a sentence.

Exercise 2

Look at these sets of words. Some mean the same thing, but there is an odd one out in each set. Draw a circle round the odd verb.

a giggle smile chuckle

b run sprint walk

c laugh grin smile

d cry weep frown

e drink sip eat

f dance jump leap

Exercise 3

Write your own verbs to complete these sentences. Try to think of something exciting!

a The cat _____ the mouse round the garden.

b The monster _____ at the children.

c Spiders are scary, because they _____ up and down on the ceiling.

d Stars are beautiful when they_____.

e The girl thought the clown was really funny and she was _____.

f The snake _____ across the rock.

Challenge

Verbs tell us about actions. Underline the verbs in these sentences.

1 The cat scratched my leg.

2 The bug climbed the wall.

3 The dog barked loudly.

Brain Teaser

Tick the verb in each set that you think is most exciting!

1 ☐ eat ☐ gobble ☐ chew

2 ☐ look ☐ watch ☐ observe

3 ☐ shout ☐ yell ☐ scream

Adjectives

Adjectives are often called describing words. They are what make your writing exciting, because you add lots of description!

Compare these two sentences:

1. I saw a spider.
2. I saw a huge, black, hairy spider.

The second sentence gives you a much clearer picture of a horrible spider!

Exercise 1

Underline the adjectives in each sentence.

a   The slimy slug crawled up the wall.

b   I bit the shiny, red apple.

c   The elephant was enormous, grey and wrinkly.

d   I hate smelly cheese!

e   He was big, bad and ugly.

f   The sparkling frost glittered in the moonlight.

g   My cat is tabby.

Top Tip *Remember, adjectives make your work exciting, and a more exciting choice of adjectives makes your work even more exciting! Look through a magazine or comic and see if you agree.*

Exercise 2

Underline the most powerful and descriptive adjective in each sentence.

a   The bath was warm/hot/scalding.

b   The dog was big/enormous/large.

c   The mouse was small/little/miniscule.

d   The story was amusing/hilarious/funny.

e   The wind was cold/freezing/icy.

Exercise 3

Look at the words in bold. Then, in the spaces, write a more exciting or interesting version.

a   The cat was **fierce**. _____   f   The spider was **scary**. _____

b   The horse was **big**. _____   g   The sun was **hot**. _____

c   The water was **cold**. _____

d   The lady was **pretty**. _____

e   The film was **good**. _____

Challenge

Choose the best adjective for each sentence.

1   Mel's tantrums are really bad/spectacular/big.

2   Mel's hair is really messy/untidy/bizarre.

3   Mel's voice is loud/noisy/ear shattering.

Brain Teaser

Underline the most exciting adjective in each pair.

1   The scorpion was huge/big.

2   The lion was ferocious/fierce.

3   The beetle was large/gigantic.

4   The water was scalding/hot.

Pronouns

A **pronoun** takes the place of a **noun**. A pronoun can also refer back to a noun. You must use the correct pronoun, so that your reader clearly understands which noun it refers to.

The most common pronouns are:

I   you   he   she   it   me   they

Look at this example.

Eleanor (noun) went to the pictures with Katie (noun).
They (pronoun) bought some popcorn.

Pronouns must agree with the noun they replace or refer back to. If the noun is **singular** (there is only one), so is the pronoun.

Lucy (noun) went to school.

Lucy is singular. So the correct pronoun would be *she*.

She (singular pronoun) went to school.

Exercise 1

Match these nouns to their pronouns. Join them with a line.

a   the cat   it

b   Mrs Jones   he

c   Stephen   me

d   we   she

e   Granny and Grandad   us

f   I   they

> **Top Tip**
> *Remember: the words **everybody, anybody, anyone, each, neither, nobody, someone** and **a person** are singular and take singular pronouns.*
>
> *For example: Everybody ought to do his or her best.*

Exercise 2

Draw a circle around the pronoun in each sentence. Careful! You may find more than one in some sentences.

a   Bethany paid some money and she went into the concert.

b   Simon and Peter like computer games. They play them all the time.

c   Alex threw his sandwich away because he didn't like it.

d   My cats play in the garden. They love pouncing on leaves!

e   I like orange juice. It tastes great.

Exercise 3

Fill in the gaps to explain who the pronouns are about.

a   David and Tina love playing football. They like to score goals!

Who are "they"? _____ and _____

b   I look after my horses carefully. I clean them out every weekend.

Who are "them"? _____

c   Ellie is three. She goes to nursery.

Who is "she"? _____

Challenge

Here are some pronouns that people use a lot:

> I me he him she you they
> them her we us.

Underline the pronouns in these sentences. Be careful though. Sometimes there's more than one!

1   He said he would come at 3pm.

2   I thought you liked them!

3   Why can't she go?

Brain Teaser

Write a pronoun in the gaps.

1   Today is my birthday.
_____ am eight today.

2   My brother and I went to the swimming baths.
_____ enjoyed the slides!

3   There are lots of spiders in the cupboard. _____ give me the creeps!

Speech marks

Speech marks show us when someone is talking.

"We can't wait for the
summer holidays!"
said Hilary.

This
tastes
great!

A speech bubble is another way of
showing us that someone is talking.

Exercise 1

Draw a line under the speech in these sentences. Then write down how you
know it is speech.

a "It's time for school!" called mum.

b "We are going to the shops," replied Kevin.

c "Would you like to come to my party?" asked Holly.

d "I don't like sprouts!" the boy cried. "I want an ice-cream!"

e "Can you help me to open this jar?" asked Granny.

f "Would you like to borrow this book?" asked the librarian.

_____

_____

*Top
Tip*

*Don't forget, speech marks are only used when someone is
actually speaking, not when their speech is being reported.*

Exercise 2

Look at these sentences. Put speech marks in the correct places.

a Put on your wellies, Jo! called mum.

b Every time we go to the swimming baths, said Harvey, I get really cold.

c Stop that! shouted the teacher.

d You are such a good footballer! sighed the girl.

Exercise 3

Write what is being said in the speech bubbles into sentences using speech marks. Use the pictures to help you.

Stop! Don't run in school!

Ahh! Aren't these kittens gorgeous!

This cookie is delicious!

a _____

_____

b _____

_____

_____

c _____

_____

_____

Challenge

Underline the words that mean *said* in these sentences.

1 "I don't want to!" howled Trevor.

2 "Why not?" Jamila whined.

Brain Teaser

Write the speech marks in the correct place.

1 What's the time, Dad? asked Julia.

2 I really like dogs, said Marie.

3 Yuck! squealed John.

Questions and exclamations

A sentence can end with a **full stop**, a **question mark** or an **exclamation mark**.

A full stop shows that the sentence is complete.

My tea is ready.

A question mark is used at the end of a sentence to show that a question is being asked.

Is tea ready yet?

An exclamation mark is used at the end of a sentence to show when something is said with a lot of expression or feeling.

"My tea was brilliant!"

Exercise 1

Complete these sentences by adding a full stop, a question mark or an exclamation mark.

a   Are we there yet____

b   It is raining heavily____

c   What was that noise____

d   Who is your best friend____

e   What do fish eat____

f   I love sherbet____

g   I hate homework____

h   Where is my coat____

i   My favourite food is curry____

PAGES 4–5

1   The answers which should be circled are: b, c and f.

2   Answers will vary, but should include useful clue words and what the objects might be.

Brain teaser
Answers will vary, but children should listen to a partner talk about school uniform or homework, before giving their own opinion.

PAGES 6–7

1   a un   f pre
     b re   g ex
     c mis   h pre
     d non   i in
     e anti   j non

2   a non   e non
     b mis   f non
     c non   g non
     d mis   h mis

3   a pre   d non
     b in   e anti
     c mis   f un

Brain teaser
     1 mis   4 un
     2 non   5 mis
     3 in

PAGES 8–9

1   a hide   d ball
     b ball   e hide
     c gum   f gum

2   a I'll   d eight
     b allowed   e eye
     c altar   f ball

3   a ewe   b flea
     c heel   d groan

Brain teaser
     1 sees   2 side
     3 their   4 to

PAGES 10–11

1   a mustn't   f you're
     b can't   g I've
     c isn't   h he's
     d shouldn't   i haven't
     e hasn't

2   a will not   e we have
     b cannot   f they will
     c she is   g has not
     d he will   h you are

3   Passage should be rewritten with the following alterations: do not, It is, has not, there is.

Brain teaser
     1 I've   2 we'll
     3 shouldn't   4 isn't

PAGES 12–13

1   a + ly = kindly
     b + ful = playful
     c + ic = heroic
     d + able = loveable
     e + worthy = blameworthy

2   a ish   f ful
     b ish   g ful
     c ful   h ish
     d ful   i ish
     e ful   j ful

3   a, b, c, e, g, h

Brain teaser
These words should be crossed out:
     1 trustish   2 wishworthy
     3 penniable

PAGES 14–15

1   Spellings should be learned using the look/say/cover/write/check method.

2   Spellings should be learned.

3   Possible answers include:
     a fat, cat, hat
     b hall, fall, call
     c hut, put, but
     d bad, sad, mad
     e pig, fig, dig
     f fin, tin, win
     g bake, lake, take

Brain teaser
     1 did, hid, kid, lid, rid
     2 fit, hit, kit, lit, nit, pit, sit, wit
     3 face, lace, pace

PAGES 16–17

1   Answers should include two of the following:
     a son, less, on
     b dance, bun, an
     c story, his, is
     d hell, she, he
     e we, the, at, eat, her
     f change, hang, an

2   Answers should include three of the following:
     a an, tan, admit, it
     b city, electric, it, elect
     c must, tar, star
     d price, rice, ice
     e did, lend, end
     f and, stand, an, tan

3   a not, an, other, her
     b arch, chive, hive, arc
     c bull, tin, let, in, bullet
     d air, plane, lane, an

Brain teaser
cart, ridge, art, rid, car

PAGES 18–19

1 a racing   d singing
   b fluttering   e walked
   c squeaking   f shining

2 a smile   d frown
   b walk   e eat
   c laugh   f dance

3 Possible answers include:
   a chased
   b spat, growled
   c climb, scamper
   d twinkle, shine
   e laughing, giggling
   f slithered

Brain teaser
   1 gobble   2 observe
   3 yell, scream

PAGES 20–21

1 a slimy
   b shiny, red
   c enormous, grey, wrinkly
   d smelly
   e big, bad, ugly
   f sparkling, glittered
   g tabby

2 a scalding   d hilarious
   b enormous   e freezing, icy
   c miniscule

3 Possible answers include:
   a ferocious   e brilliant
   b massive   f terrifying
   c freezing   g scalding
   d gorgeous

Brain teaser
   1 huge   2 ferocious
   3 gigantic   4 scalding

PAGES 22–23

1 a it   d us
   b she   e they
   c he   f me

2 a she   d My, They
   b them   e I, It
   c he, it

3 a David and Tina   b horses
   c Ellie

Brain teaser
   1 I   2 We
   3 They

PAGES 24–25

1 a It's time for school!
   b We are going to the shops
   c Would you like to come to my party?
   d I don't like sprouts. I want an ice-cream!
   e Can you help me to open this jar?
   f Would you like to borrow this book?

   Because they have speech marks around them.

2 a "Put on your wellies, Jo!" called mum.

   b "Every time we go to the swimming baths," said Harvey, "I get really cold."
   c "Stop that!" shouted the teacher.
   d "You are such a good footballer!" sighed the girl.

3 Possible sentences include:
   a "Stop! Don't run in school!" said the teacher.
   b "Ahh! Aren't these kittens gorgeous!" sighed Emma.
   c "This cookie is delicious," munched Peter.

Brain teaser
   1 "What's the time, Dad?" asked Julia.
   2 "I really like dogs," said Marie.
   3 "Yuck!" squealed John.

PAGES 26–27

1 a ?   f !
   b .   g !
   c ?   h ?
   d ?   i .
   e ?

2 a .   d !
   b !   e !
   c .   f .

3 a !   d ?
   b .   e !
   c ?

Brain teaser
   Possible answers include:
   1 How old are you?
   2 I'm called Elizabeth.
   3 Look out!

PAGES 28–29

1 Passage should be read carefully.

2 a the liver of a Nyamatsane
   b many, long, hot, lonely days
   c slaughters and skins it

3 Answer can be yes or no, as long as the answer is justified.

Brain teaser
   1 a gasping fish
   2 Because the woman was greedy and drank all of the water, so there was no water for the animals.

PAGES 30–31

1 whispered, squealed, hissed, shrieked, replied, laughed

2 a mumbled   d exclaimed
   b cheered   e shrieked
   c sighed

3 Answers will vary.

Brain teaser
   Possible answers include:
   1 moaned   2 shivered
   3 screamed

PAGES 32–33

1 a buzzed   d crying
   b running   e barking
   c stroked   f flapped

2 a P   d P
   b A   e P
   c A   f A

3
  a past   **d** past/present
  b future   **e** future
  c present   **f** present

Brain teaser
walked, looking, run, barking, climbed, look, fell, appeared, jumped

PAGES 34–35
1   **a** 3   **e** 7
      b 2   **f** 5
      c 4   **g** 6
      d 1

2   so, Then, After that, Finally

3   First, Danny got up and had breakfast. Then he got dressed. After that he watched TV. Next he telephoned Beth to see if she wanted to play football. Then they went to the park. Eventually they bought crisps and lemonade at the café. Finally they went home and played computer games.

Brain teaser
Possible answers include:
1 also   **2** because
3 after that

PAGES 36–37
1   Possible answers include:
We went to the 2pm pantomime and it cost £24.50. There was one interval when we bought ice-cream and sweets. The panto finished at 4.30pm. After that we got the bus home.

2   I was at the aquarium. There were lots of fantastic fish. I liked the shark tunnel best. The café had lots of tasty food, like crisps and squashy cakes. I bought a toy shark to bring home. I travelled home on the train.

3   The correct order is: b, e, d, c, a, f.

Brain teaser
A recount in the past tense, in chronological order, of an event.

PAGES 38–39
1   An example of planning if, for example, The Three Little Pigs was chosen (could be done with different story) would be:
  a the three pigs
  b at the three pigs' houses
  c the heroes = pigs;
     villain = wolf
  d the wolf dresses up as a pig and manages to get into the pigs' houses
  e The pigs get the wolf to help them make a pie (the pigs realise that the new pig is actually the wolf) and the pigs push the wolf into the pie. They cook it and have wolf pie.

2   There are many answers to all questions. Examples for the adapted Three Little Pigs tale are:
  a three
  b Because they're clever (depending on the tale used).
  c one, the wolf
  d Because he plans to kill the pigs.
  e James, Andrew, Alex (pigs)
     The wolf is called William.
  f James, Andrew and Alex are little pink pigs. William is grey and has large, fanged teeth.
  g Wolf: "I am going to eat you whole." Pigs: "Not if we have anything to do about it."

3   Child should write a story containing the elements discussed in the previous questions.

Brain teaser
A variety of answers such as: The heroes are Cinderella, the prince, the fairy godmother and the animals that get turned into the coachmen. The villains are the evil stepmother and the ugly step-sisters. The problem is that the stepmother and step-sisters are cruel to Cinderella and will not let her go to the Ball.

PAGES 40–41
1   A letter using formal language, with no contractions, no slang, and finished with "Yours faithfully".

2   A letter using informal language, which can include "chatty" language and slang, and may finish with "love".

3   Dear Mrs Nelson,

  <u>We take great pleasure</u> inviting you to our prize-giving ceremony. Your son Paul has won a prize for mathematics. We know <u>you will</u> share our pride in this achievement, and <u>look forward to</u> seeing you.

  <u>Yours faithfully,</u>

  Mr H. Master

  <u>Hi</u> Sam!

  <u>Guess what?</u> <u>I'</u>ve won a prize for maths! Amazing, <u>eh</u>? Mum's <u>chuffed</u>, so <u>I'll</u> be in her good books for a bit! Are you coming to stay soon?

  <u>Talk to you later,</u>

  Paul

Brain teaser
1 a formal letter
2 an informal letter
3 a formal letter

PAGES 42–43
1   Possible answers include: blizzard, white, blanketed, hushed, snowman, toboggan.

2   A diagram of a snowman with a poem inside.

3   Many answers are possible, such as the shape of a snake with a snake poem inside, or a football with a football poem inside.

Brain teaser
A diagram of a spider with a poem inside.

ANSWERS

TEST PRACTICE

PAGE 44
Spellings

Learn the spellings! Use look/say/cover/write/check, as an aid.

PAGE 45
Handwriting

The handwriting exercise should be neat with all of the letters clearly identifiable.

PAGES 46–47
Story writing

Plan the story using the techniques discussed. This must include a strong beginning and end. Careful thought and consideration of the character's appearance, attitude and what the villains / heroes are like. Where is the story set? What problem does the hero have to overcome and how does the hero overcome the problem?

PAGES 48–49
Comprehension

1 You need sugar, a spoon, warm water, a cup and saucer, food colouring and a thread.
2 *Evaporate* refers to when water seems to disappear into the air.
3 You leave it somewhere warm so the crystals carry on growing.
4 The spoon is to tie to the thread so that the crystal will dangle into the water.
5 Four verbs are: growing, tie, leave, pour.
6 Diagram of pictures showing the instructions.

PAGE 50
Writing letters

1 Remember to include formal language, and what is wrong with the service.
2 Use informal language. It could start with "Hi" and finish with "Love from".

Letts Educational
4 Grosvenor Place, London SW1X 7DL
Orders: 015395 64910
Enquiries: 015395 65921
Email: enquiries@lettsandlonsdale.co.uk
Website: www.lettsandlonsdale.com

First published 2009

Editorial and design: 2ibooks [publishing solutions] Cambridge

Author: Lynn Huggins-Cooper
Book concept and development: Helen Jacobs, Publishing Director
Editorial: Sophie London, Senior Commissioning Editor
Katy Knight, Junior Editor
Illustrators: Andy Roberts and Phillip Burrows
Cover design: Angela English

British Library Cataloging in Publication Data. A CIP record of this book is available from the British Library.

ISBN 9781844192342

Text, design and illustration © 2009 Letts Educational Ltd

Printed in Malta

Letts Educational make every effort to ensure that all paper used in our books is made from wood pulp obtained from well-managed forests, controlled sources and recycled wood or fibre.

Exercise 2

Complete these sentences by writing in either a full stop or an exclamation mark.

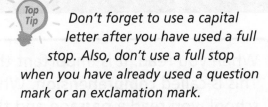

a It has rained all week____

b Don't do that____

c I like cats____

d My party was so exciting____

e It was the scariest film I had ever seen____

f Bats are nocturnal animals____

Exercise 3

Now complete these sentences by writing in a full stop, a question mark or an exclamation mark.

a It was the most amazing thing I have ever seen____

b Sherbet lemons are my favourite sweets____

c What's your name____

d How can I help you____

e Wow____

Challenge

Add an exclamation mark or a question mark to each of these sentences.

1 Is it time to go now

2 What's that awful smell

3 That was so loud, I jumped out of my skin

Brain Teaser

Write some sentences of your own that finish with either a full stop, a question mark or an exclamation mark.

1 _____

_____

2 _____

_____

3 _____

_____

Understanding text

When you read, it is important that you **understand** what you are reading. This is called **comprehension**. When you do a comprehension exercise at school, you read a passage and then answer questions to show you have understood what you have read.

Exercise 1

Read this passage. Then have a go at Exercise 2 and Exercise 3.

A great warrior is asked by his pregnant wife for the liver of a Nyamatsane – she craves it. She begs him, saying he must prove he loves her – and that he is the greatest warrior – by hunting a Nyamatsane. He warns that great evil will come of this deed, but the next day he takes his assegai and begins his search. For many long, hot, lonely days he searches – and all at once finds the Nyamatsane dwellings. An old Nyamatsane has been left alone, and he slaughters and skins it, placing its liver in a hide bag. He hears the creatures returning and hides under the skin. They sniff and search, smelling a strange man smell, but are unable to find him. He pretends to eat pebbles, like the creatures, hiding them all the while in his bag.

The hunter creeps away when they curl up to sleep. When the Nyamatsanes find the skin he left behind, they chase with bloodcurdling whoops and cries. The hunter throws down a sparkling pebble from his bag that turns into a glass tower – with him on top! Loyal hunting dogs chase the Nyamatsanes away and the hunter returns to his village.

The wife eats the liver, but then develops a burning thirst. She drinks until no water is left in the village. She ran down to the pounding river – and drank it dry! That night, the animals came out into the cool night air and found the water had gone. A gasping fish tells them what happened. In a rage, they thunder into the village and devour the hunter and his wife – and justice is done.

Exercise 2

Now answer these questions.

a What does the warrior's wife ask him for?

_____

b Which words let us know that the hunter searches for a long time? Copy them out here:

_____

c What does the warrior do to the old Nyamatsane?

_____

Exercise 3

At the end of the story, it says *and justice is done*. Do you think the ending is fair? Explain your answer.

_____

_____

_____

_____

_____

_____

When you are answering a comprehension, write in full sentences. Read the passage once. Then read the questions and skim the passage again looking for words that might help you to answer.

Challenge

Make up a comprehension test for a friend or family member, using your favourite story.

Brain Teaser

1 Who tells the animals what has happened?

_____

2 Why do you think the animals were angry?

_____

_____

Synonyms for said

"Hello," said Sam. "Hello," said Mel. "What shall we do today?" said Sam. "I don't know," said Mel.

Gets a bit boring when you repeat the same word – *said* – over and over again, doesn't it?

To make dialogue (when people are talking) more interesting, we can use **synonyms** for the word *said*. Synonyms are different words that mean the same thing.

All these words can be used instead of *said*:
roared whispered
shouted bellowed
uttered replied
muttered explained

Exercise 1

Underline all of the words that mean *said* in the paragraph below.

"What's that?" whispered Fay. "I don't know – but I don't like it!" squealed

Ellie. "Perhaps it's a burglar!" hissed Fay. "Cleo!" shrieked Ellie, as a little

tortoiseshell cat ran into the room. "Mieow?" the cat replied. "We thought

you were an intruder!" laughed Fay.

Exercise 2

Use the words in the box below to complete the sentences. Think about which words meaning *said* fit best with the meaning of the sentences.

> cheered   mumbled   exclaimed   shrieked   sighed

a "Where is the bathroom?" _____ Susie quietly.

b "Hurray! Goal!" _____ Alex as his team scored.

c "Ooh, it's gorgeous!" _____ Katie. "I'm really envious!"

d "Sorry," _____ Peter. "I didn't mean it."

e "Yuck! A spider!" _____ Dave.

 Top Tip *Make sure you know how full stops, capital letters and speech marks work when you are using dialogue! Look at the Glossary on page 51 to help you.*

Exercise 3

Now choose four sentences from Exercise 2, but this time use your own words to fill in the gaps. Think of the sense of the sentence before you choose.

a _____

b _____

c _____

d _____

Challenge

Choose a *said* word to complete these sentences:

1 "It's a rat," _____ Julie.

2 "Are we nearly there yet?" _____ Sophie.

3 "If we're quiet, they might not see us!" _____ Helen.

Brain Teaser

Find a better word to replace *said* in these sentences.

1 "It's hot!" said Ben.

_____

2 "Brrr! I'm really cold," said Anna.

_____

3 "A snake!" said Jane.

_____

Active and passive verbs

Remember, **verbs** are words that describe actions.

| The bird is flying. | Flying is the verb, because it tells us about what the bird is doing. |

| The cat chased the bird. | Chased is the verb, because it tells us what the cat did. |

Verbs can be active or passive.

| The cat walked across the garden. | An active verb tells you what is being done by someone or something. |

| The girl was kissed by her granny. | A passive verb tells you about the person or thing the action is being done to. |

Verbs change to show us what tense – past, present or future – is being used.

I am looking is the present tense. It is happening now.

I looked is the past tense. It has already happened.

I will look is the future tense. It hasn't happened yet.

Exercise 1

Underline the verbs in these sentences.

a The fly buzzed past my face.

b The boy is running along the road.

c The cat was stroked.

d The baby is crying.

e Some dogs were barking.

f A group of bats flapped through the trees.

Exercise 2

Look at these sentences. Write A if you think the verbs are active and P if you think they are passive.

a _____ The fish was caught.

b _____ The horse neighed.

c _____ Worms wriggle on the ground.

d _____ The windows were cleaned.

e _____ The baby was cuddled.

f _____ The boy laughed.

> **Top Tip**
> Remember, verbs are vital. A sentence must have a verb in it to be a proper sentence. You can even have sentences that are one word long – if that word is a verb.
>
> Help! Go! Stop!

Exercise 3

Write down which verb tense is being used in these sentences.

a The sun shone yesterday. _____

b The girl will sing later. _____

c I am dancing. _____

d The hamster hid in its bedding. _____

e The tomato will get squashed. _____

f Everyone is watching. _____

Challenge

Can you tell whether verbs are active or passive? Underline the active verbs in these sentences.

1 The girl laughed.

2 The door was closed gently.

3 The sun shone brightly.

Brain Teaser

Read the passage below and underline all of the verbs.

I walked down the road, looking around for my dog. He had run off, barking wildly. As I climbed over a wall to look for him, I fell over. Suddenly, he appeared and jumped on top of me.

Reports and conjunctions

Reports about things that have happened need to tell the reader what happened and in what order. They must be accurate and the words you use should keep it interesting for the reader.

Reports use words called **conjunctions** to join sentences, linking them together. These give the reader a sense of the order things happen in.

Conjunctions may be used to:

add to an idea

summarise ideas

explain or illustrate a point

arrange ideas in order

make comparisons and contrasts

Conjunctions include words such as:

and, then, next, eventually, finally, yet, because, so, however

Exercise 1

Imagine you are a reporter for the school newspaper. You have to write a report about sports day. You have written your notes, but they have been mixed up. Put them in the correct order, using the boxes to number the sections.

a   After break, the children came out onto the field.

b   By morning break the parents started to fill the seats on the field.

c   The children lined up for the first race – the egg and spoon!

d   Sports day dawned bright and sunny.

e   It was a great day, enjoyed by everybody.

f   It was won by Judith Nelson.

g   Many more exciting races were run before everyone went home.

Exercise 2

Try to make this report more interesting. Use the conjunctions in the box to fill in the gaps. This will tell your readers the order that things happened in.

> then   so   after that   finally

It was a sunny afternoon. Rosie was hot,

_____ she bought an ice-cream.

_____ she decided to go swimming.

_____ she felt a bit cooler. On the way home, she bought

an ice-lolly. _____, she felt cool and comfortable!

Top Tip *Remember, then can be useful but it is horribly over-used! "I went to the sweet shop, then I went to the cake shop, then I went to the park and then I went home."*

Exercise 3

Now, on a separate piece of paper, write a report of Danny's day using his diary entry. Use the conjunctions in the box to give your readers an idea of the order things happened in.

> first   after that   then   eventually   next   finally

7.30 Got up and had breakfast.
7.45 Got dressed.
8.00 Watched TV.
9.00 Telephoned Beth to see if she wanted to play football
in the park.
2.00 Went to the park and bought crisps and lemonade at the café.
4.00 Went home and played computer games.

Challenge

"My school report was awful! My mum said that, until it was better, I would not be allowed out to play." Can you find the conjunction in the last sentence?

Brain Teaser

Think of a conjunction for each of these groups. Write them in the gaps.

1   add to an idea _____

2   explain or illustrate a point _____

3   arrange ideas in order _____

Recounts

A **recount** tells us about an event.

A recount is written in the order in which things happened.

A recount is written in the past tense.

On Saturday night, Jack and his family had a barbecue. They started to get ready at about 3 o'clock. Mum collected wood for a bonfire and Dad made a big salad. Jack and his Dad went to the shops late in the afternoon to buy some burgers and ice-cream. They chose tutti-frutti. They had to hurry to the baker's shop to get some buns because it shut at 5 o'clock. When they got home, Dad lit the barbecue. Mum and Jack lit some candles in the garden and they waited for their friends to arrive.

Exercise 1

Look at the information below. It gives details about a trip to the pantomime. Now use the space to write a recount of this event.

Cost: family ticket £24.50. Started at 2pm and finished at 4.30pm. One interval. Ice-cream and sweets for sale. Bus home.

_____

_____

_____

_____

_____

_____

Exercise 2

This recount has been written in the present tense by mistake. Write it out again, changing it to the past tense. You may need another sheet of paper for this exercise.

> I am at the aquarium. There are lots of fantastic fish. I like the shark tunnel best. The café has lots of tasty food, like crisps and squashy cakes. I am buying a toy shark to bring home. I am travelling home on the train.

_____

_____

_____

_____

Exercise 3

This recount has been written in the correct tense, but it is jumbled up and not in the correct order. Re-write it on a sheet of paper in the correct order.

a   On the way home, we bought some sweets.

b   I went to the park.

c   "Shall we play football?" she said.

d   When I got there I saw my friend Tracey.

e   I took a ball with me.

f   When we got home, Mum asked Tracey if she'd like to stay to tea.

Top Tip _A recount is in chronological order (the order in which things happened). It is told in the past tense._

Challenge

Write about your day. Fill something in for each time given.

8am _____

9am _____

12 noon_____

1.30pm_____

6pm _____

8pm _____

Brain Teaser

Think of an event you have enjoyed and write a recount of it on a sheet of paper. Do you have a school newspaper or magazine? They may be interested!

Writing stories

Do you like reading traditional tales, myths and legends from all over the world? These traditional stories often have common themes, especially where good triumphs over evil!

Traditional tales usually have a beginning like this:

"A long time ago ..."   "There once was ..."

The stories are full of heroes and villains. There is often a long journey and there is usually a great problem to solve.

Have you read *Beauty and the Beast*, *Pinocchio* and *Hansel and Gretel*? What problems had to be solved in these stories?

Exercise 1

You are going to plan your own traditional tale, by adapting one that you already know. You could choose *Cinderella*, *Sleeping Beauty*, *The Three Little Pigs*, or any other traditional tale you know well! You can make up new characters, add new events or even change the way one of the characters acts. If you choose *The Three Billy Goats Gruff*, for example, the troll could be really scared of the goats, who keep teasing him! In the box below plan the outline of your tale.

Top Tip *Look for myths, legends and traditional tales on the Internet. Try www.nationalgeographic. com/grimml/ for some great versions of 12 traditional tales.*

Exercise 2

Now make notes on a sheet of paper about the characters in your tale. Use the guidelines to help you.

a   How many heroes are there?

b   Why are they heroes?

c   How many villains are there?

d   Why are they villains?

e   What are the names of your characters?

f   What do they look like?

g   What kind of things do they say?

Exercise 3

Now write your tale. Write a rough draft first, then, when you're ready, you can write it on a computer or a sheet of paper. If you like, you can add in some illustrations (drawings). When your story is finished, try to learn it by heart. Then tell it to an audience – just like they did in the old days.

Challenge

Write a synopsis – a short description containing the main events – of your favourite traditional tale here:

_____

_____

_____

_____

Brain Teaser

Think about the story of Cinderella. Name the heroes and villains. Then explain the problem that had to be overcome.

Who were your favourite characters? Why?

Letters

Formal letters are the type of thing sent by your school, to tell the adults you live with about reports or meetings. They contain formal language.

Informal letters are the type of chatty letters you send to friends. They contain informal language.

Dear Mrs Nelson,

We take great pleasure inviting you to our prize-giving ceremony. Your son Paul has won a prize for mathematics. We know you will share our pride in this achievement, and look forward to seeing you.

Yours faithfully,

Mr H. Master

Hi Sam!

Guess what? I've won a prize for maths! Amazing, eh? Mum's chuffed, so I'll be in her good books for a bit! Are you coming to stay soon?

Talk to you later,

Paul

Exercise 1

Imagine you have built a fabulous wildlife garden. Write a formal letter below to invite the Prime Minister to your school. Remember to use formal language – no contractions (*isn't*, *can't* and so on). Finish the letter *Yours faithfully*.

_____

_____

_____

_____

_____

_____

Exercise 2

Now write an informal letter telling your auntie that the Prime Minister is coming to visit your school. Remember to use informal language or your auntie might think you are cross with her!

_____

_____

_____

_____

_____

_____

_____

_____

_____

_____

Top Tip _Look at letters from school and see if you can spot the formal language._

Exercise 3

Look at the formal and informal letters opposite. Underline the things that tell you whether the letter is formal or informal.

Challenge

When you write to relatives and friends, you can be informal.

Write a letter to a member of your family. Remember to use informal language or they might think that you are cross with them!

Brain Teaser

Formal or informal?

1 Which sort of letter would start _Dear Sir_?

_____

2 Which sort of letter would end _Love from_?

_____

3 Which sort of letter would end _Yours faithfully_?

_____

Shape poems

Shape poems are poems that are written in the shape of the thing being written about.

A leaf poem could be written in the shape of a leaf.

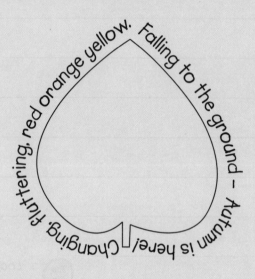

Exercise 1

Write a poem about winter. Think of six words to do with snow and cold weather. Then write them below. Some words have already been suggested to get you started.

icicle   sparkle   glittering   frosty

Exercise 2

Now write your poem from Exercise 1 in the shape of a snowman. Use the shape below to guide you.

Look for shape poems on the Internet. Just type 'shape poems' into a search engine and see what pops out!

Exercise 3

Write a shape poem about something you are interested in. It could be snakes, new clothes, football – you choose. Write some words in this box to get you started. Then, on a piece of paper, draw your shape and write in your poem.

Challenge

Can you write a shape poem about a big hairy spider?

Write some words to use in the poem below.

Brain Teaser

Write your poem in the shape of a spider here.

Spellings

The words being tested are:

cooking	chopped	touch
show	pieces	remove
soap	thick	pastry
measure	juicy	tight
began	apple	straight
golden	gently	several
weigh	boil	squares

Ask an adult to read this passage to you while you listen. Then, the adult should read the passage again, this time pausing after each underlined word so you can write down how it is spelled on a separate piece of paper.

Susie was appearing on the children's <u>cooking</u> <u>show</u> *Sticky Fingers*. Her Mum was going to help her. They washed their hands thoroughly with <u>soap</u>, and then started to <u>measure</u> things out carefully. They <u>began</u> with <u>golden</u> sugar. Susie asked her Mum to <u>weigh</u> out some butter, which they then <u>chopped</u> into <u>pieces</u>. They added <u>thick</u>, <u>juicy</u> slices of <u>apple</u> to a pan of water, which they brought <u>gently</u> to the <u>boil</u>.

"Don't <u>touch</u>, Mum! It's hot!" Susie laughed. "Now – we need to <u>remove</u> the cores from these other apples, and pack them into the <u>pastry</u> case, nice and <u>tight</u>. Try to cut <u>straight</u> pieces. Cut <u>several</u> <u>squares</u> to put on the pie as decoration."

Handwriting is assessed as a part of other tests – so it is a good idea to practise!

Copy out the section of a poem shown below on a piece of paper, in your best handwriting. Try to make all of the ascenders (the long sticks on letters such as *d* and *k*) and descenders (the long tails on letters such as *p* and *g*) on the letters an equal size.

That's My Boy!

The whistle shrieks, and we're off!
Charging after the ball
A herd of cartoon hippos
Churning the field to mush.

I break away from the pack
Dodge left, feint right,
Blazing up the field, turbo charged.
With a blast – it's in the net!

I whirl, arms outstretched,
Whooping boys tangle round my neck.
I slip and wriggle downwards
Peering into the boiling crowd.

The joy fossilises in my chest,
Falls, and lodges in my gut
Cold, like the ice pack Sir carries for injuries.
My Dad missed it.

Wait – arms and legs pumping,
Tie flying ludicrously over his shoulder,
A familiar shape is running across the field.
He's shouting something I can't quite hear.

Then his voice booms, and people turn to look.
"Attaboy!" He's shouting. "That's my boy!"

He's here! He's here!

Story writing

Choose one of the story titles below and write a story. Spend 10 to 15 minutes planning the story and 35 minutes writing it. Use the planning sheet to help you. Try to keep your writing neat! You will need spare paper to write your story.

Titles

Lost in the snow

A kitten for Christmas

Space slug!

Drifting

Where is the story set?

Who are the main characters? What are they like?

Is there a problem to solve, or a challenge to face?

An exciting opening:

A good strong ending:

Think of some descriptions to use in your story:

interesting words brainstorm

Comprehension

Grow your own gems!

You need: sugar, spoon, warm water, cup and saucer, food colouring, thread.

1 Put some warm water in a cup.

2 Add a few drops of food colouring.

3 Stir in some sugar. Keep adding until no more will dissolve in the water.

4 Pour a little of the mixture into a saucer and put it in a warm place – on the radiator or on a sunny window sill. Cover the rest of the mixture and put it somewhere cool.

5 When the water evaporates (disappears into the air), you will be left with some small crystals.

6 Choose the biggest crystal. Then ask an adult to help you tie it onto a piece of thread.

7 Tie the other end of the thread to a spoon. Rest the spoon across the top of the cup of water. The crystal will dangle from the thread, into the water.

8 Leave the cup somewhere warm and the crystal will keep growing!

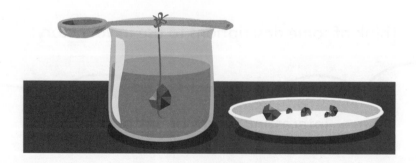

1 What do you need in order to grow your own gems? Make a list. (1 mark)

_____

2 What does the word _evaporate_ mean? (1 mark)

_____

3 Why do you have to leave the mixture somewhere warm? (1 mark)

_____

4 What is the spoon used for? (1 mark)

_____

5 Find and make a list of four verbs in the instructions. (2 mark)

_____

_____

6 Draw step-by-step pictures to present the instructions in a different way. You may write captions beneath the pictures, but you should try to give as much information as possible in a visual way – using pictures. (4 mark)

**Total
10 marks**

Writing letters

Choose **one** letter to write from the two choices below:

1   A formal letter to complain about bad service in a fast food restaurant. Don't forget to use formal language, and to set your address out properly!

_____

_____

_____

_____

_____

_____

2   An informal letter telling a friend about a great party. Remember, you should use informal language!

_____

_____

_____

_____

_____

_____

_____

adjective Describing word, used to make sentences more interesting. The fluffy (adjective) cat (noun) purred

apostrophe ' Shows that a letter or letters are missing from words. *Is not* becomes *isn't* (the apostrophe replaces the o). *She has* becomes *she's* (the apostrophe replaces the ha). See contractions. It is also used as the possessive, such as *the cat's tail*

brainstorm Jotting down notes at the beginning of a writing task to help you to get organised.

capital letter Upper case letter. For example, ABC is used for names and places

comma , A punctuation mark. It shows where you need to pause in a sentence

comprehension understanding what a text is about

conjunction a word used to link sentences or clauses, or to correct words within a phrase

contractions Shortened versions of words with letters left out shown by an apostrophe: couldn't, wouldn't, isn't

exclamation mark ! A punctuation mark. It shows feeling, like surprise or shock

fiction Stories that have been made up

full stop . A punctuation mark. It tells you when a sentence has ended

homonyms Words that have the same spelling but different meanings, for example, pick can mean: choose carefully, a tool, detach (pick fruit)

homophones Words that have different spellings but sound alike – for example: bear/bare, pair/pear, grate/great

lower case Letters that are not capitals, for example, abc

non-fiction Reports, recipes and instructions. They tell us facts. They are not made up like fiction

noun The naming word – a thing, person or place. Book (thing), Lynn (person), Durham (place)

plural Describing more than one. The cats' tails

prefix The letters that you put before a word that already exists to change its meaning. For example, the prefix pre is used before the word paid (prepaid) to mean paid in advance

pronoun A word to replace a noun. It can also refer back to a noun. The most common pronouns are: I, you, he, she, it, we and they

punctuation The marks that divide words up into phrases and sentences – for example, full stop . comma , exclamation ! question mark ?

question mark ? A punctuation mark. It tells you that a question is being asked

recount a report that describes events in chronological order, or the order in which they happened

singular Describing one thing. A cat is singular. Some cats is plural

speech marks " " punctuation marks that surround direct speech. Other punctuation goes inside them, e.g. "Goodbye," said Mum

suffix The letters that you can put at the end of an existing word, such as *ly*. Suffixes can often change nouns to adjectives

syllables Chunks of sound in a word. Alligator has four: all/ig/at/or

synonym A word that means almost the same as another word, for example, shut, slam, close. Synonyms make your writing much more interesting

upper case Upper case letters are capitals, for example, ABC

verb Action (or doing) words such as: talking, washing, playing